30⁰⁰
4-83

# R. CALDECOTT'S PICTURE BOOK

(No. 1)

CONTAINING

THE DIVERTING HISTORY OF JOHN GILPIN

THE HOUSE THAT JACK BUILT

AN ELEGY ON THE DEATH OF A MAD DOG

THE BABES IN THE WOOD

LONDON

FREDERICK WARNE AND CO., Ltd.

AND NEW YORK

*Printed in Great Britain*

# THE DIVERTING HISTORY

OF

# JOHN GILPIN:

*Showing how he went farther than he intended, and came safe home again.*

JOHN GILPIN was a citizen
   Of credit and renown,
A train-band captain eke was he,
   Of famous London town.

John Gilpin's spouse said to her dear,
   " Though wedded we have been
These twice ten tedious years, yet we
   No holiday have seen.

" To-morrow is our wedding-day,
   And we will then repair
Unto the ' Bell ' at Edmonton,
   All in a chaise and pair.

" My sister, and my sister's child,
   Myself, and children three,
Will fill the chaise ; so you must ride
   On horseback after we."

The Linendraper bold

He soon replied, " I do admire
  Of womankind but one,
And you are she, my dearest dear,
  Therefore it shall be done.

" I am a linendraper bold,
  As all the world doth know,
And my good friend the calender
  Will lend his horse to go."

4

Quoth Mrs. Gilpin, "That's well said;
   And for that wine is dear,
We will be furnished with our own,
   Which is both bright and clear."

John Gilpin kissed his loving wife;
   O'erjoyed was he to find,
That though on pleasure she was bent,
   She had a frugal mind.

he morning came, the chaise was
    But yet was not allowed   [brought,
o drive up to the door, lest all
    Should say that she was proud.

o three doors off the chaise was stayed,
    Where they did all get in;
x precious souls, and all agog
    To dash through thick and thin.

nack went the whip, round went the
    Were never folks so glad!  [wheels,
he stones did rattle underneath,
    As if Cheapside were mad.

John Gilpin at his horse's side
    Seized fast the flowing mane,
And up he got, in haste to ride,
    But soon came down again;

For saddletree scarce reached had he,
    His journey to begin,
When, turning round his head, he saw
    Three customers come in.

So down he came; for loss of time,
    Although it grieved him sore,
Yet loss of pence, full well he knew,
    Would trouble him much more.

The 3 Customers

7

'Twas long before the customers
　　Were suited to their mind,
When Betty screaming came downstairs,
　　"The wine is left behind!"

"Good lack!" quoth he, "yet bring it
　　My leathern belt likewise,　　[me,
In which I bear my trusty sword
　　When I do exercise."

Now Mistress Gilpin (careful soul!)
　　Had two stone bottles found,

To hold the liquor that she loved,
　　And keep it safe and sound.

Each bottle had a curling ear,
　　Through which the belt he drew,
And hung a bottle on each side,
　　To make his balance true.

Then over all, that he might be
　　Equipped from top to toe,
His long red cloak, well brushed and
　　He manfully did throw.　　[neat,

8

Now see him mounted once again
Upon his nimble steed,
Full slowly pacing o'er the stones,
With caution and good heed.

But finding soon a smoother road
Beneath his well-shod feet,
The snorting beast began to trot,
Which galled him in his seat.

"So, fair and softly!" John he cried,
    But John he cried in vain;
That trot became a gallop soon,
    In spite of curb and rein.

So stooping down, as needs he must
    Who cannot sit upright,
He grasped the mane with both his
    And eke with all his might. [hands,

His horse, who never in that sort
    Had handled been before,

What thing upon his back had got,
    Did wonder more and more.

Away went Gilpin, neck or nought;
    Away went hat and wig;
He little dreamt, when he set out,
    Of running such a rig.

The wind did blow, the cloak did fly
    Like streamer long and gay,
Till, loop and button failing both.
    At last it flew away.

Then might all people well discern
    The bottles he had slung;
A bottle swinging at each side,
    As hath been said or sung.

The dogs did bark, the children screamed,
    Up flew the windows all;
And every soul cried out, "Well done!"
    As loud as he could bawl.

Away went Gilpin—who but he?
    His fame soon spread around;
"He carries weight! he rides a race!
    'Tis for a thousand pound!"

And still as fast as he drew near,
    'Twas wonderful to view
How in a trice the turnpike-men
    Their gates wide open threw.

And now, as he went bowing down
  His reeking head full low,
The bottles twain behind his back
  Were shattered at a blow.

Down ran the wine into the road,
  Most piteous to be seen,
Which made the horse's flanks to
  As they had basted been. [smoke,

But still he seemed to carry weight,
　　With leathern girdle braced ;
For all might see the bottle-necks
　　Still dangling at his waist.

Thus all through merry Islington
These gambols he did play,
Until he came unto the Wash
Of Edmonton so gay ;

And there he threw the wash about
On both sides of the way,
Just like unto a trundling mop,
Or a wild goose at play.

At Edmonton his loving wife
    From the balcony spied
Her tender husband, wondering much
    To see how he did ride.

"Stop, stop, John Gilpin!—Here's the
    They all at once did cry; ⌈house!"
"The dinner waits, and we are tired;"
    Said Gilpin—"So am I!"

But yet his horse was not a whit
    Inclined to tarry there;
For why?—his owner had a house
    Full ten miles off, at Ware.

So like an arrow swift he flew,
    Shot by an archer strong;
So did he fly—which brings me to
    The middle of my song.

Away went Gilpin, out of breath,
  And sore against his will,
Till at his friend the calender's
  His horse at last stood still.

The calender, amazed to see
  His neighbour in such trim,
Laid down his pipe, flew to the gate,
  And thus accosted him:

"What news? what news? your tidings
  Tell me you must and shall— [tell;
Say why bareheaded you are come,
  Or why you come at all?"

Now Gilpin had a pleasant wit,
  And loved a timely joke;
And thus unto the calender
  In merry guise he spoke:

"I came because your horse would
    And, if I well forebode, [come :
My hat and wig will soon be here,
    They are upon the road."

The calender, right glad to find
    His friend in merry pin,
Returned him not a single word,
    But to the house went in ;

Whence straight he came with hat and
    A wig that flowed behind,   [wig,
A hat not much the worse for wear,
    Each comely in its kind.

He held them up, and in his turn
    Thus showed his ready wit :
"My head is twice as big as yours,
    They therefore needs must fit."

"But let me scrape the dirt away,
    That hangs upon your face;
And stop and eat, for well you may
    Be in a hungry case."

Said John, " It is my wedding-day,
    And all the world would stare
If wife should dine at Edmonton,
    And I should dine at Ware."

So turning to his horse, he said
    " I am in haste to dine;

'Twas for your pleasure you came here
    You shall go back for mine."

Ah! luckless speech, and bootless boast
    For which he paid full dear;
For while he spake, a braying ass
    Did sing most loud and clear;

Whereat his horse did snort, as he
    Had heard a lion roar,
And galloped off with all his might,
    As he had done before.

Away went Gilpin, and away .
Went Gilpin's hat and wig;
He lost them sooner than at first,
For why?—they were too big.

Now Mistress Gilpin, when she saw
Her husband posting down
Into the country far away,
She pulled out half-a-crown;

And thus unto the youth she said
That drove them to the "Bell,"
"This shall be yours when you bring
My husband safe and well." [bac

The youth did ride, and soon did meet | But not performing what he meant,
    John coming back amain; |     And gladly would have done,
Whom in a trice he tried to stop, | The frighted steed he frighted more,
    By catching at his rein. |     And made him faster run.

Away went Gilpin, and away
    Went postboy at his heels,
The postboy's horse right glad to miss
    The lumbering of the wheels.

Six gentlemen upon the road,
    Thus seeing Gilpin fly,
With postboy scampering in the rear,
    They raised the hue and cry.

"Stop thief! stop thief! a highwayman!"
　　Not one of them was mute;
　And all and each that passed that way
　　Did join in the pursuit.

And now the turnpike-gates again
    Flew open in short space;
The toll-man thinking, as before,
    That Gilpin rode a race.

And so he did, and won it **too,**
    For he got first to town;
Nor stopped till where he had got up
    He did again get down.

Now let us sing, Long live the King.
And Gilpin, long live he;
And when he next doth ride abroad,
May I be there to see.

# THE HOUSE
# THAT JACK BUILT

# THIS is the House that Jack built.

2

This is the Malt,
That lay in the House that
Jack built.

This is the Rat,
That ate the Malt,
That lay in the House
that Jack built.

8

This is the Cat,

That killed the Rat,

That ate the Malt,

That lay in the House that Jack built.

This is the Dog,

That worried the Cat,

That killed the Rat,

That ate the Malt,

That lay in the House that

Jack built.

This is the Cow with the crumpled horn,

That tossed the Dog,

That worried the Cat,

That killed the Rat,

That ate the Malt,

That lay in the House that

Jack built.

This is the Maiden all forlorn,
That milked the Cow with the crumpled horn,

That tossed the Dog,
That worried the Cat,
That killed the Rat,
That ate the Malt,
That lay in the House
that Jack built.

This is the Man all tattered and torn,
That kissed the Maiden all forlorn,
That milked the Cow with
    the crumpled horn,
That tossed the Dog,
That worried the Cat,
That killed the Rat,
That ate the Malt,
That lay in the House
    that Jack built.

23

This is the Priest, all shaven and shorn,
That married the Man all tattered and torn,
That kissed the Maiden all forlorn,

That milked the Cow with
the crumpled horn,
That tossed the Dog,
That worried the Cat,
That killed the Rat,
That ate the Malt,
That lay in the House that
Jack built.

This is the Cock that crowed in the morn
That waked the Priest all shaven and shorn,
That married the Man all tattered and torn,
That kissed the Maiden all forlorn,
That milked the Cow with
the crumpled horn,
That tossed the Dog,
That worried the Cat,
That killed the Rat,
That ate the Malt,
That lay in the House that
Jack built.

This is the Farmer who sowed the corn,

That fed the Cock that crowed in the morn,

That waked the Priest all shaven and shorn,

That married the Man all tattered and torn,

That kissed the Maiden all forlorn,

That milked the Cow with the crumpled horn,

That tossed the Dog,

That worried the Cat,

That killed the Rat,

That ate the Malt,

That lay in the House

that Jack built.

# AN ELEGY ON
# THE DEATH OF A MAD DOG

# An ELEGY
## on the DEATH of
# a MAD DOG.

WRITTEN
By
Dʳ GOLDSMITH

PICTURED
By
R. CALDECOTT

SUNG
By Master
BILL PRIMROSE

IN MEMORY OF
TOBY

GOOD people all, of every sort,
Give ear unto my song;
And if you find it wondrous short,

It cannot hold you long.

In Islington there lived a man,
    Of whom the world might say,
That still a godly race he ran,

Whene'er he went

to pray.

A kind and gentle heart he had,
To comfort friends and foes;
The naked every day he clad,

When he put on

his clothes

And in that town a dog was found :
As many dogs there be —

Both mongrel,           puppy,           whelp,

and hound,

And curs of low degree.

This dog and man at first were friends;

But, when a pique began,

The dog, to gain some private ends,

Went mad, and bit the man.

Around from all

the neighbouring streets

The wondering neighbours ran;

And swore the dog had lost his wits,

To bite so good a man.

The wound it seem'd both sore and sad
To every christian eye;

And while they swore the dog was mad,

They swore the man would die

But soon a wonder came to light,
That show'd the rogues they lied—

The man recover'd of the bite;

The dog it was that died.

# THE BABES
# IN THE WOOD

SORE SICKE THEY WERE
AND LIKE TO DYE

# The
# BABES IN THE WOOD.

NOW ponder well, you parents deare,
    These wordes which I shall write;
A doleful story you shall heare,
    In time brought forth to light.

A gentleman of good account
    In Norfolke dwelt of late,
Who did in honour far surmount
    Most men of his estate.

Sore sicke he was, and like to dye,
    No helpe his life could save;
His wife by him as sicke did lye,
    And both possest one grave.

No love between these two was lost,
    Each was to other kinde;
In love they liv'd, in love they dyed,
    And left two babes behinde:

The one a fine and pretty boy,
    Not passing three yeares olde;
The other a girl more young than he
    And fram'd in beautye's molde.

The father left his little son,
    As plainlye doth appeare,
When he to perfect age should come
    Three hundred poundes a yeare.

And to his little daughter Jane
    Five hundred poundes in gold,
To be paid downe on marriage-day,
    Which might not be controll'd:

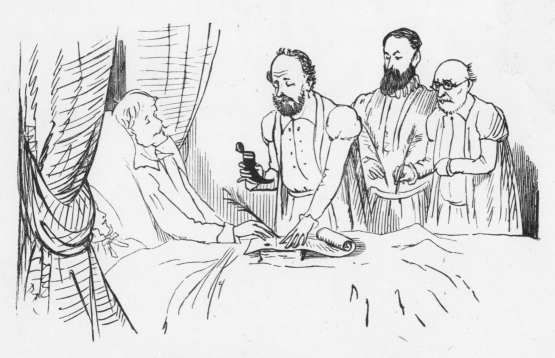

But if the children chanced to dye,
    Ere they to age should come,
Their uncle should possesse their wealth;
    For so the wille did run.

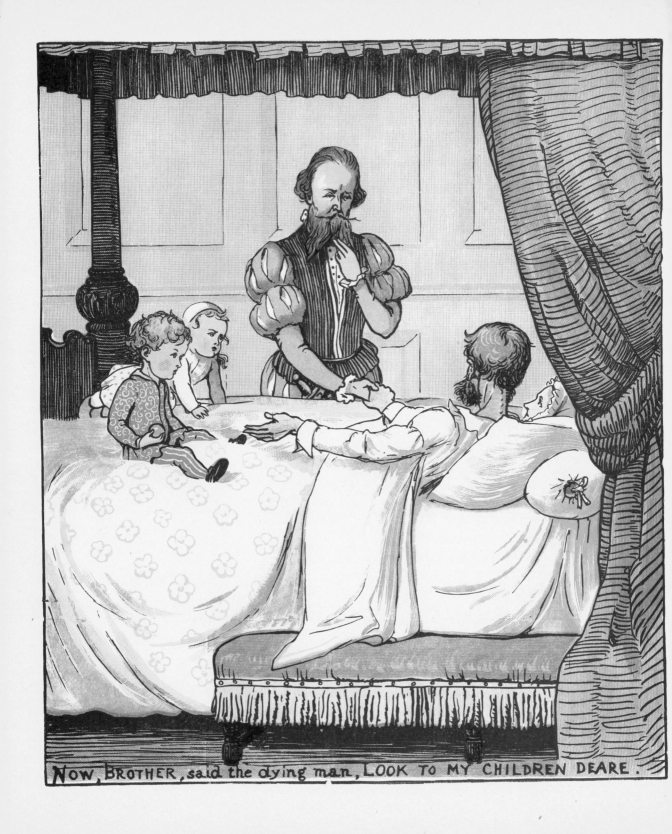

Now, BROTHER, said the dying man, LOOK TO MY CHILDREN DEARE.

"Now, brother," said the dying man,
    "Look to my children deare;
Be good unto my boy and girl,
    No friendes else have they here:

"To God and you I do commend
    My children deare this daye;
But little while be sure we have
    Within this world to staye.

"You must be father and mother both,
    And uncle all in one;
God knowes what will become of them,
    When I am dead and gone."

With that bespake their mother deare :

"O brother kinde," quoth shee,

"You are the man must bring our babes

To wealth or miserie :

"And if you keep them carefully,
    Then God will you reward ;
But if you otherwise should deal,
    God will your deedes regard."

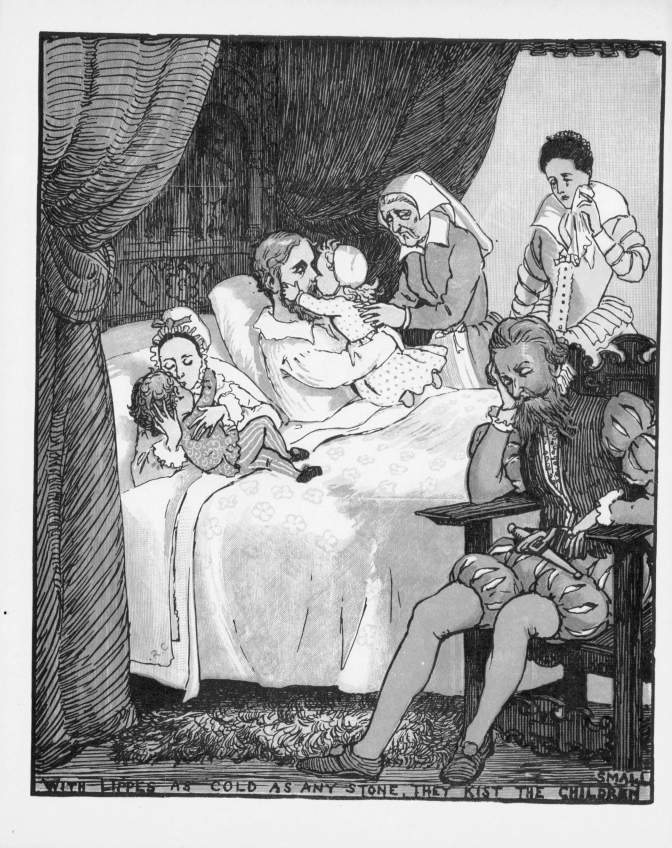
WITH LIPPES AS COLD AS ANY STONE, THEY KIST THE CHILDREN

SMALL

With lippes as cold as any stone
   They kist the children small :
"God bless you both, my children deare ; "
   With that the teares did fall.

These speeches then their brother spake
    To this sicke couple there :
" The keeping of your little ones,
    Sweet sister, do not feare :

"God never prosper me nor mine,
       Nor aught else that I have,
  If I do wrong your children deare,
       When you are layd in grave."

THEIR PARENTS BEING DEAD & GONE, THE CHILDREN HOME HE TAKES.

The parents being dead and gone,
The children home he takes,
And bringes them straite unto his house,
Where much of them he makes.

He had not kept these pretty babes
A twelvemonth and a daye,
But, for their wealth, he did devise
To make them both awaye.

He bargain'd with two ruffians strong,
    Which were of furious mood,
That they should take the children young,
    And slaye them in a wood.

He told his wife an artful tale,
    He would the children send
To be brought up in faire London,
    With one that was his friend.

Away then went those pretty babes,
    Rejoycing at that tide,
Rejoycing with a merry minde,
    They should on cock-horse ride.

AWAY THEN WENT THE PRETTY BABES
REJOYCING AT THAT TIDE

They prate and prattle pleasantly
    As they rode on the waye,
To those that should their butchers be,
    And work their lives' decaye:

So that the pretty speeche they had,
  Made murderers' heart relent :
And they that undertooke the deed,
  Full sore did now repent.

Yet one of them, more hard of heart,
  Did vow to do his charge,
Because the wretch, that hired him,
  Had paid him very large.

The other would not agree thereto,
So here they fell to strife;
With one another they did fight,
About the children's life:

And he that was of mildest mood,
Did slaye the other there,
Within an unfrequented wood,
Where babes did quake for feare!

AND HE
THAT WAS OF
MILDEST
MOOD
DID SLAYE THE OTHER THERE

He took the children by the hand,
     While teares stood in their eye,
And bade them come and go with him,
     And look they did not crye:

And two long miles he ledd them on,

    While they for food complaine :

"Stay here," quoth he, "I'll bring ye bread,

    When I come back againe."

These prettye babes, with hand in hand,
Went wandering up and downe ;

But never more they sawe the man
Approaching from the town.

Their prettye lippes with blackberries
Were all besmear'd and dyed;

And when they sawe the darksome night,
They sat them downe and cryed.

Thus wandered these two prettye babes,
Till death did end their grief;
In one another's armes they dyed,
As babes wanting relief.

No burial these prettye babes
Of any man receives,

Till Robin-redbreast painfully
Did cover them with leaves.

IN ONE ANOTHER'S ARMS THEY DYED.